Riches of the AMAZON

Written by
CHRISTOPHER SWEENEY

Illustrated by
LEIGH DRAGOON

This story is set in the 21st century, in the Amazon rainforest, Brazil. Each chapter ends with a non-fiction page that gives more information about Brazil, the rainforest environment and its people.

OXFORD
UNIVERSITY PRESS

JUSTIN VANDERBERG

JOANNA VANDERBERG

JORGE RAMIREZ

PAOLO QUEIJO

XU'XULO

QI'QIRU

FICTIONAL CHARACTERS

JUSTIN VANDERBERG: A 12-year-old boy who visits Brazil with his mother. Justin suffers from epilepsy.

JOANNA VANDERBERG: Justin's mother. She is a senior executive of Tormincorp, a mining company that wants to open a gold mine in the Brazilian rainforest.

JORGE RAMIREZ: An ethnobiologist who acts as Tormincorp's guide to the rainforest and its people.

PAOLO QUEIJO: A Brazilian man who is also a senior executive of Tormincorp.

XU'XULO: The leader of the Yolungo tribe – (fictional) people of the Amazon rainforest.

QI'QIRU: A young Yolungo woman who speaks up for her people.

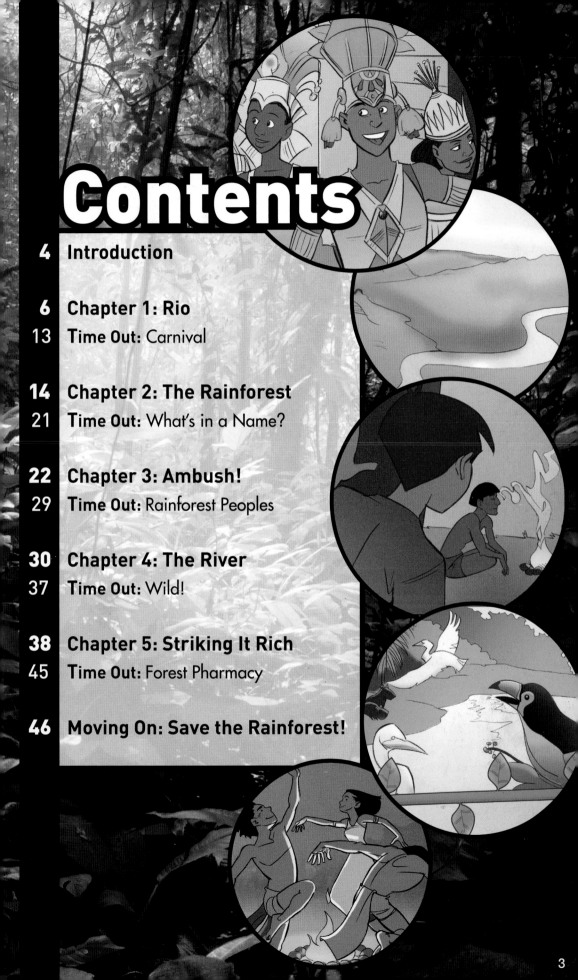

Contents

The Amazon River is the world's largest river. During the rainy season, the Amazon can swell up to 40 kilometres wide. For this reason, it is often called the 'river sea'.

This great river snakes its way through the Amazon rainforest, a gigantic tropical forest that covers an area of about 5.2 million square kilometres. The rainforest is extremely rich in plant and animal life.

Although the rainforest is one of the great treasures of the planet, it is being destroyed. Trees are cut down for their wood and to make space for cattle ranches. Mines are dug into the earth for gold and other minerals.

TIMELINE

6000 BC/BCE >>	AD/CE 1500 >>	1532 >>	1541 >>	1695 >>
Humans begin to settle in the Amazon basin at this time or earlier.	Pedro Alvarez Cabral of Portugal lands on the Brazilian coast by accident.	The Portuguese begin to settle in Brazil. Within 100 years, 90% of indigenous peoples die off.	Francisco de Orellana of Spain explores – and names – the Amazon River.	Gold is first discovered in Brazil.

The Amazon isn't only a home to plants and animals. There are human beings who have lived there for thousands of years. Their way of life is now being destroyed along with the rainforest.

Here's a story about one such group of people and how they helped defend the riches of the Amazon.

This story is set in an actual time in history, although some of the events are fictional. Real events during this period are shown on the timeline below.

1822 >>	1970 >>	1988 >>	1997 >>	2006 >>
Brazil gains independence from Portugal.	Deforestation (cutting down trees) in the Amazon rainforest begins to take place.	Environmentalist Chico Mendes is murdered when he tries to prevent logging.	Brazil forces illegal gold miners off the lands of the indigenous Yanomami people.	Brazil protects 15 million hectares of rainforest – the largest rainforest preserve in the world.

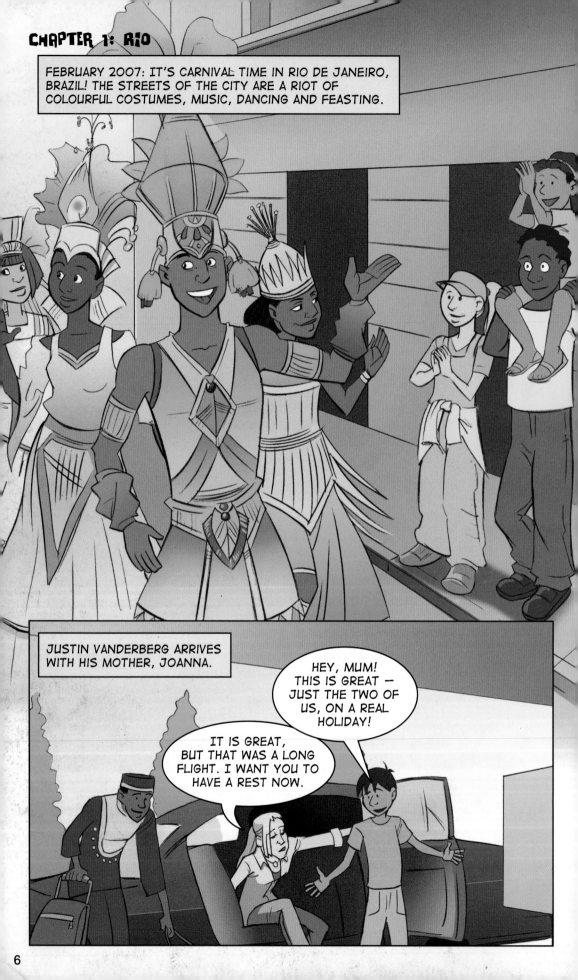

FEBRUARY 2007: IT'S CARNIVAL TIME IN RIO DE JANEIRO, BRAZIL! THE STREETS OF THE CITY ARE A RIOT OF COLOURFUL COSTUMES, MUSIC, DANCING AND FEASTING.

JUSTIN VANDERBERG ARRIVES WITH HIS MOTHER, JOANNA.

HEY, MUM! THIS IS GREAT — JUST THE TWO OF US, ON A REAL HOLIDAY!

IT IS GREAT, BUT THAT WAS A LONG FLIGHT. I WANT YOU TO HAVE A REST NOW.

CARNIVAL

For four days every year, the streets of Rio de Janeiro swirl with the fun and excitement of the Carnival. Thousands of people put on colourful costumes and celebrate non-stop!

Carnival ('goodbye to meat') is celebrated before the start of Lent, the 40 days before Easter when Christians traditionally avoid eating meat. Since people usually kicked up their heels and had a good time before Lent, 'carnival' also came to mean a time of merry-making!

The fun begins when the mayor of Rio gives the keys of the city to Rei Mumo, the person chosen to be King of Carnival. A grand tradition of the Carnival is the Samba Parade. It goes on for two days and 70,000 people take part!

CHAPTER 2: THE RAINFOREST

THE MIGHTY AMAZON RIVER SNAKES THROUGH THE LARGEST RAINFOREST IN THE WORLD!

THE NEXT DAY, JUSTIN AND JOANNA ARE IN THE RAINFOREST AT THE CAMP OF TORMINCORP.

SO I HAVE TO SPEND MY HOLIDAY IN A MINING CAMP!

THERE ARE LOTS OF REASONS. THE MINE WILL POLLUTE THEIR LAND.

THE PLANTS AND ANIMALS THEY DEPEND ON WILL BE DESTROYED.

YOU SEEM TO KNOW A LOT ABOUT THIS.

I'VE MET WITH THE YOLUNGO MANY TIMES.

THEIR SHAMAN XU'XULO (CHU CHU LO) HAS TAUGHT ME A LOT.

SHAMAN XU'XULO?

HE'S THEIR LEADER. THERE HE IS!

THE MEETING BEGINS. JORGE TRANSLATES FOR THE YOLUNGO.

QI'QIRU SAYS SHE'S NOT AGAINST THE MINE. BUT SHE WANTS TO BE CONSULTED ON EVERYTHING.

WHY IS A CHILD SPEAKING FOR ALL OF YOU?

YOU PEOPLE DON'T OWN THE RAINFOREST, YOU KNOW!

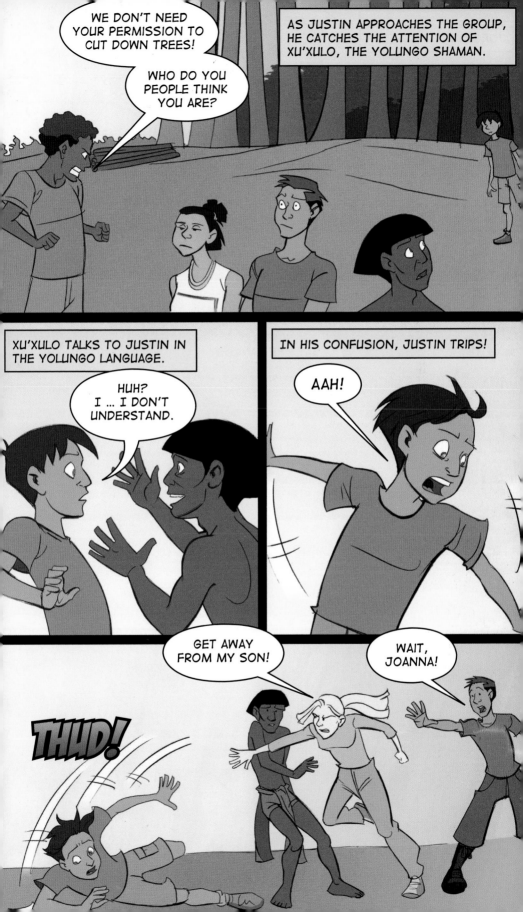

WHAT'S IN A NAME?

In 1541, the Spanish explorer Francisco de Orellana travelled through the area. He claimed that he saw a group of people whose women fought fiercely alongside the men. He named the river Amazon, after a Greek myth about a race of warrior women.

No one knows for sure which group of people de Orellana saw. It may have been the Tapuya people, whose men and women fight together. The Yagua is another possibility. Yagua men wear grass skirts, and this may have confused de Orellana.

Two Yagua men

XU'XULO WARNS THE VILLAGERS.

A FIGHT TAKES PLACE BETWEEN THE MINE WORKERS AND THE YOLUNGO!

WHERE ARE YOU TAKING ME?

XU'XULO LEADS JUSTIN AWAY FROM THE FIGHTING.

SLOW DOWN! I CAN'T KEEP UP!

WHOA!

JUSTIN!

RAINFOREST PEOPLES

Kayapo Chief

The indigenous peoples of the Amazon have lived in the rainforest for thousands of years. As parts of the rainforest are 'developed', it becomes harder for them to follow their way of life. Here are a few peoples who remain.

Kayapo
- Farmers who live south of the Amazon Basin in Brazil
- Men wear discs in their lower lips
- The Kayapo have successfully prevented mining and logging on their lands

Maku
- Nomads who live in the northwestern part of the Amazon
- Hunters shoot poison darts from blowguns
- Some fear the Maku people are on the brink of extinction

Penare
- Hunter-gatherers who live in the Amazon basin of Venezuela
- The women avoid learning Spanish so their culture will be kept alive
- The men weave baskets with geometric and animal patterns

31

XU'XULO POINTS OUT ALL KINDS OF ANIMALS, BIRDS, INSECTS AND PLANTS — MORE THAN JUSTIN EVER DREAMED EXISTED.

THEY SEE A JAGUAR ...

HEY, LOOK AT THAT TURTLE!

AND THE WORLD'S LARGEST RODENT, THE CAPYBARA, COMING DOWN TO THE RIVER FOR A DRINK ...

AND THE WORLD'S BIGGEST SNAKE, THE ANACONDA, HAVING ITS MIDDAY MEAL.

WOW! LOOK!

XU'XULO GRABS JUSTIN'S HAND AS AN ALLIGATOR SWIMS BY.

BACK AT THE TORMINCORP CAMP ...

JOANNA, QI'QIRU SAYS SHE SAW JUSTIN LEAVE WITH XU'XULO LAST NIGHT.

WHERE DID THEY GO?

OH, NO! THE WITCH DOCTOR KIDNAPPED HIM!

DOES QI'QIRU KNOW WHERE THEY WENT? HE NEEDS HIS MEDICINE.

YES, TO ANOTHER YOLUNGO VILLAGE DOWNSTREAM.

SHE'S OFFERING TO TAKE YOU THERE.

WILD!

The Amazon is home to amazing animals that are not found anywhere else in the world.

Vampire Bat
- It comes out at night to dine on its favourite food – blood!
- Its saliva contains a substance that prevents blood from clotting.
- Its nose has a special heat sensor for detecting juicy spots on its prey.

Anaconda
- The world's biggest snake – it can weigh as much as a cow!
- Like other boa constrictors, it squeezes the life out of its prey.
- This snake swallows its prey whole, then digests for weeks – burp!

Three-toed Sloth
- The world's least active mammal – it spends 80% of its time resting.
- It moves so slowly, moths live in its fur and moss grows on it.
- Predators such as jaguars and anacondas don't notice it because it hardly moves!

THE BOAT DRIFTS SLOWLY DOWNSTREAM.

I WANTED TO GET RID OF THE WITCH DOCTOR. HE GOT AWAY, BUT I'LL GET HIM YET!

SO WHAT QI'QIRU TOLD ME WAS RIGHT. YOU PLANNED THE ATTACK BY THE MINE WORKERS!

WHAT ARE YOU PLANNING TO DO, PAOLO? TIE US UP AND LEAVE US HERE IN THE MIDDLE OF NOWHERE?

YES! THAT'S EXACTLY WHAT I'M PLANNING TO DO!

SUDDENLY, JORGE ATTACKS!

AARGH!

THAT EVENING, JUSTIN IS THE GUEST OF HONOUR AT THE YOLUNGO VILLAGE.

AT THE START OF THE MEAL ...

YOU WANT ME TO DRINK THAT?

I GUESS IT WOULD BE RUDE TO REFUSE, EH?

GLUG! GLUG!

OH, IT'S THAT STUFF YOU GAVE ME BEFORE! WHAT IS IT?

SUDDENLY, THERE IS A COMMOTION.

WHAT'S HAPPENING?

41

Annatto flower

FOREST PHARMACY

The indigenous peoples of the Amazon are experts at using rainforest plants as medicines. The shamans or native healers use their knowledge of plants to treat everything from toothache and snake bites to cuts and burns.

Sometimes, a single plant has many uses. For example, the annatto tree is used to treat eye infections, skin diseases and liver problems. It lowers blood pressure, aids digestion and is a treatment for epilepsy.

These cures have the potential to save lives. Scientists are working with native healers to develop new drugs for cancer, heart disease and other illnesses.

Many of these plants exist nowhere else on Earth and they are known only to the American Indians who live in the Amazon. It's just one more reason to save the rainforest and its peoples!

Save the

Every year, large areas of the Amazon rainforest are cut down to clear land for cattle ranches, farms, roads and towns. As this habitat is removed, many plant and animal species are becoming extinct – some before they are even discovered.

The indigenous peoples of the Amazon are also disappearing. After thousands of years, their way of life is being lost, along with their knowledge of the rainforest.

Scientists worry that the cutting down of forests is adding to climate change. Living trees help to purify the air and trap carbon dioxide, a greenhouse gas that causes global warming. When trees are cut down and burned, however, the carbon trapped in them is sent back into the atmosphere.

What can we do to stop deforestation? Environmentalists suggest using recycled paper, eating less meat and campaigning to protect forests.

Are you ready for action?

Rainforest!

A logging operation in the Amazon rainforest

Deforestation in the Amazon

INDEX

GLOSSARY

carnival – a festival, often with a procession of people in fancy clothes

destroy – to put an end to something completely

diverse – different kinds of something

epilepsy – a disease of the nervous system

extinct – to no longer exist

indigenous – to come from, be a native of, a particular place

mine – a place where coal, metal and other natural materials are dug out of the ground

poison – something that can harm or kill a living thing if taken into the body

pollute – to make something, for example, the air or water, dirty

ritual – actions used in a ceremony

seizure – a sudden fit which may be caused by epilepsy

sympathy – understanding another person's feelings